Why flamingoes have red legs

and other stories

Hannie Truijens

Illustrated by Pat Nessling

Nelson

Nelson Thornes Ltd
Delta Place
27 Bath Road
Cheltenham GL53 7TH
United Kingdom

Text © J. C. M. Truijens 1989
Illustrations © Macmillan Education Ltd 1989
This edition: illustrations © Thomas Nelson and Sons Ltd 1992
Illustrated by Pat Nessling

First published by Macmillan Education Ltd 1989
ISBN 0–333–48468–1

This edition first published by Thomas Nelson and Sons Ltd 1992

Reprinted in 2001 by Nelson Thornes Ltd

ISBN 0-17-400569-5
06 07 08 09 / 19 18 17 16 15 14 13 12

Printed in Croatia by Zrinski

Why flamingoes have red legs

Whenever the Indians had a feast the animals watched and listened from a safe distance.

One day the animals decided that they also wanted to have a big feast.
They agreed to hold the feast at the river when the moon was full.
There would be music and a big campfire.

The owl asked, "Who will fetch wood and look after the fire so that we have enough light to dance by?"

"We won't need a fire," said the monkey, "it will be full moon."

The wise old vulture said, "Won't we eat
each other? Won't the termite die in
fright when it sees the anteater?
Won't the frog tremble when it sees the
stork, and the fly when it sees the frog?
It won't work."

"Why not?" asked the anteater, who
loved to dance.
"Surely we can promise not to eat each other on
the night of the feast. Anyone who breaks the
rules will be punished."

4

"Yes," said the jaguar,
"I'll eat up anyone who breaks the rules.
"I'll do it with great pleasure."
The monkeys looked at him in horror.
All the animals were quiet.
It was a good idea.
Nobody would dare to break the rules.
The jaguar was really looking forward
to the feast. He would be able to
show off his lovely spotted hide.
He also hoped that some of the animals might
just forget and break the rules.

5

The parrots and the snakes were also
waiting to show off their beautiful feathers
and colourful skins in the full light of the moon.
The animal feast would be as good as
the feast of the Indians.

There was not much time left.
All the animals were busy decorating themselves.
The frogs and the tortoises painted
themselves from head to foot.

The monkeys made necklaces and
bracelets from stones.
The bald vulture made a feather headband to
hide his bald head and the crocodile
decorated himself with flowers.

Only the flamingoes, who still had white
legs, didn't know how to decorate themselves.
They went to the owl to ask for his help.

At first the owl refused to help them.
Then he said, "I may have something for
those long legs of yours.
If my feet weren't too big I would have
worn them myself.
But I will have to think about it."

The flamingoes begged and pleaded and
at last the owl said, "All right, I'll help you.
But you must promise me that you won't stop
dancing the whole night long.
If you do, you'll be in trouble."

The flamingoes said, "We'll dance without stopping from one full moon to the other."

The owl said nothing. He went into his hollow and came out with some snake skins in his beak. They were striped red, white and black.

The flamingoes pulled the skins over their legs. They fitted well and made lovely stockings.

They left with the stockings hidden under their wings, and the owl grinned wickedly.

At last it was full moon and
the feast could begin.
The anteater played on his flute, the
rattlesnake rattled his rattle.
The monkeys beat the time on the coconuts, the
crocodile beat on the big drum and the frogs
croaked loudest of all.
The dancers walked around to show off
their decorations. Then they bowed to each
other and started to dance.

They all danced as well as they could.
The jaguar hopped around on his hind
legs until he was dizzy.
The sloth slowly swayed to and fro.
The vulture strutted around proudly with
the headband on his bald head.
The fish in the river leaped out of the
water to join in the dance. The monkeys
held tails and danced in a ring.

But one of the coral snakes wasn't
happy. She crawled up to the dancing
flamingoes and peered at their legs.
She tried to make them stop dancing.
The flamingoes remembered the words of the
owl and didn't stop.

At last one of the flamingoes tripped
and fell flat on the ground. This is what
the coral snake had been waiting for.

12

"Come and look, all of you," shouted
the coral snake. "The flamingoes
are wearing snake skins.
They killed some of our sisters to decorate
themselves for the feast. They are vain and
cruel and they must be punished."

The coral snakes rushed to attack the
legs of the flamingoes and to tear off the
snakeskin stockings. They were so
fierce that even the jaguar stood with his
mouth open.

The coral snakes bit the legs of the flamingoes with their poisonous fangs. The wounds burned like fire and the flamingoes screamed with pain. With their last strength they dragged themselves to the river to cool their red and painful legs in the water.

The angry coral snakes couldn't follow them into the water and waited for the flamingoes on the banks of the river.

From that day on, coral snakes always crawl around on the banks of rivers, hoping that one day the flamingoes will come back on land. But the coral snakes are waiting in vain.

Although the wounds have healed, the legs of the flamingoes are still red and still burn. And that is why flamingoes have red legs and always stand in the water.

How the birds got their colourful feathers

Long, long ago, when the sun first
warmed the rocks, the flowers, the animals
and the people with her rays, she also
gave them their lovely colours.
The grass shone like a green emerald, the
clouds sailed through the sky like white
llamas and even the jaguar, who didn't really
deserve it because he was so cruel,
could show off with his lovely shiny hide.

But the sun had forgotten the birds.
They still flew around in their grey feather
suits, and were ashamed of themselves.
They complained from morning to night, but the
sun didn't seem to hear them.

Then one day the birds called a big
meeting. They decided to fly to the sun to
beg her for some colours.

The birds prepared themselves for the long flight. The condor and the eagle flew in front and showed the way.

Three birds stayed at home. The weaver bird hadn't finished his nest. The nightingale didn't mind his dull colour, and spent all his time singing. The humming bird couldn't fly that far with his small wings.

The birds flew higher and higher.
At first the sun was warm on their
feathers. Then it became hotter and hotter.
They would have burnt themselves if the sun
hadn't seen them in time.

The sun took pity on the birds. She
called together all the clouds.
She woke up the wind. The wind blew the
clouds against each other, and it started to
rain on earth.

The sun didn't wait long. She threw
her rays between the raindrops and a rainbow
appeared above the birds.
The rainbow shone with red, orange,
yellow, green, blue and violet.
"Look, the sun has heard us," cried the
birds. The eagle was the first to fly into
the rainbow.

Each bird looked for the colours it
liked most and tried them on.
The cardinal birds soaked themselves in red, the
canaries dipped themselves in yellow and
the kingfishers quickly flew through and
came out blue and pink.
The toucans ended up with red
and yellow beaks, and
to this day the parrots still have all the
colours of the rainbow.

When at last all the birds had the
colours they wanted, they thanked the
sun with their songs.
Then they spread their wings and flew home.
The sun laughed and sent her rays to dry and
warm them.

To this day the birds sing every morning to
thank the sun for giving them their colours.

And what happened to the three birds
that stayed at home?
The weaver bird still hasn't finished
his nest and the nightingale still spends all
his time singing.

And the humming bird?
The humming bird also got a colourful
suit of feathers even though he stayed at
home. This is how it happened.

Some drops of the rainbow fell into
the flowers from which the humming bird
sucks honey with his long beak.
When he sucked the honey out of the flowers, the
drops of rainbow fell on his feathers.
They have stayed there to this day.

The weaver bird

The weaver bird weaves a beautiful
nest. He plasters it on the inside with mud
and then lines it with feathers.
He sings a beautiful song and walks around
proudly, with his head in the air, just
like a person.

This is not so very strange. As every
Guarani Indian knows, the weaver bird was
once one of them. This is how it happened.

At the beginning of time the brave Jaebe
lived in the jungle with his father.
Every day Jaebe went hunting while his
father looked for berries and fruit.
The two of them were happy and contented.
But one day this changed.
    Jaebe had hunted right to the
edge of the forest and when he came to
a river he sat down to rest.
He saw the tall grass moving on the
other side of the river.

Suddenly a girl walked out of the grass. She was lovelier than all the flowers in the jungle. She went to get water from the river, turned around and walked away into the grass.

Jaebe waited there for the rest of the day to see if she would come back. She didn't.

After that Jaebe came to the river every day, hoping to see the lovely girl again. She never came.

Jaebe's father saw that there was something wrong with his son.

"What's troubling you, my son?" he asked. "You are as silent as the shadow of the moon."

"I saw a lovely girl at the river," said Jaebe, "and I want to see her again."

His father nodded. "I should have known. It is time for you to look for a bride. I will see to it that you get the loveliest bride of all."

Jaebe's father took him to the village.

"All the young braves will compete today," he said to Jaebe. "The winner will marry the loveliest girl of all, the daughter of the chief."

The chief's daughter came out of the hut, dressed in flowers from head to toe.

"That is not the girl from the river," said Jaebe.

"You will compete for the chief's daughter," ordered his father angrily.

Every Indian son obeys his father, so Jaebe did what he was told.

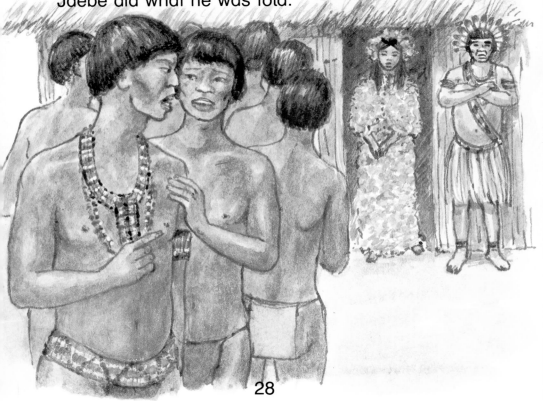

Jaebe passed the first round. He was one
of the few braves who could hit the far target.
In the second round they had to swim across a wild river.
Only Jaebe and Tata, the bravest boy from the
village, were able to cross the river.

The chief said to Jaebe and Tata,
"This is the hardest part. You must try to
stay without food or water for ten days.
You may choose the place where you want
to fast."

Tata went to his hut to fast and
Jaebe chose to fast in a hollow tree.
Before he crawled into the tree he looked around.
Then he saw her – the girl from the river.
"What is your name?" he asked her.
"Ipona," she answered.
Jaebe smiled at her and then went into the
hollow tree. Ipona sat in front of the
tree and waited.
After eight days Tata gave up. He could
not fast any longer. Jaebe was still in his
hollow tree and Ipona was still waiting.

At the end of the tenth day the chief and his daughter went to the hollow tree.

"Come out now Jaebe," called the chief. "You have won and will marry my daughter."

Jaebe came out of the tree, took Ipona by the hand and walked to the chief.

"I do not want your daughter," he said. "My heart belongs to Ipona."

The chief was very angry and ordered Jaebe to be tortured to death. The braves dragged Jaebe away from Ipona.

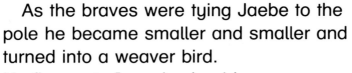

As the braves were tying Jaebe to the pole he became smaller and smaller and turned into a weaver bird.
He flew onto Ipona's shoulder.

"Jaebe, I would have gone into the other world with you," she cried.
"Why have you changed?"
Then Ipona also turned into a weaver bird and the two birds flew away together, singing.

And today, when the Guarani Indians hear two weaver birds sing together, they tell the story of Jaebe and Ipona.